Scene 1

The Big Bad Advert Wolf enters.

Big Bad Advert Wolf: Hello, I'm the Big Bad Wolf. Are you sick and tired of the same old boring trip to see grandma? Need a wolf to eat someone you know? Then call today. And remember – *who's* afraid of the Big Bad Wolf? *You* are!

Everyone comes on singing and takes up position as forest.

All: Who's afraid of the big bad wolf, the big bad wolf, the big bad wolf? Who's afraid of the big bad wolf? La La La La La!

Freeze as forest and woodland creatures.

Narrator 1: *(Steps forward.)* This is the story of Little Red Riding Hood.

Good Little Red 1: Hello. I'm Little Red Riding Hood.

All: *(Clapping and cheering.)* Yay!

Good Little Red 1: Oh thank you!

Bad Wolf 1: Hello. I'm the Big Bad Wolf.

All: *(Boo and hiss in melodramatic fashion.)* Boo. Hiss.

3

Bad Wolf 1:	Oh be quiet.
Mad Granny 1:	I'm blind, I'm old, I'm deaf, I'm dumb. My teeth are gone, can't eat a crumb. I'm grandma … Get the picture?
Bad Wolf 1:	I'm hungry … Get the picture?
Mad Granny 1:	*(Chasing him around the forest)* You're not eating me, sonny.
Bad Wolf 1:	Aaahhh!!!
Mad Granny 1:	You're not eating me sonny.
Bad Wolf 1:	Aaahhh!!!
Mad Granny 1:	Take that, you old wolf.
Bad Wolf 1:	Help!

Everyone skips around the stage, singing.

All:	Who's afraid of the big bad wolf, the big bad wolf, the big bad wolf? Who's afraid of the big bad wolf? La La La La La!

Freeze as forest and woodland creatures.

Narrator 2:	This is the story of Little Red Riding Hood.
Bad Little Red 1:	Hello. I'm Little Red Riding Hood.
All:	*(Clapping and cheering)* Yay!
Bad Little Red 1:	Oh thank you.
Sad Wolf:	Hello. I'm the Big Bad Wolf.
All:	*(Boo and hiss in melodrama fashion)* Boo. Hiss.
Sad Wolf:	Oh be quiet.
Bad Little Red 1:	*(Picking on Wolf)* Call yourself a wolf, huh? C'mon then, let's see you scare me.
Sad Wolf:	Leave me alone.
Bad Little Red 1:	Come on. Bet you can't.
Sad Wolf:	*(Growls at her)* Rrroouww!!
Bad Little Red 1:	*(Laughing)* Is that the best you can do? Wolfie's a scaredy cat.
Sad Wolf:	Am not.
Bad Little Red 1:	Are too.
Sad Wolf:	Am not.
Bad Little Red 1:	Are too.
Sad Wolf:	*(Stomps foot)* Go away!

Everyone skips around the stage singing …

5

All:	Who's afraid of the big bad wolf, the big bad wolf, the big bad wolf? Who's afraid of the big bad wolf? La La La La La!

Freeze as forest and woodland creatures.

Scene 3 ⎯⎯⎯⎯⎯⎯⎯⎯⎯⎯⎯⎯⎯⎯⎯⎯

Narrator 3:	This is the story of Little Red Riding Hood.
Good Little Red 2:	Hello. I'm Little Red Riding Hood.
All:	*(Clapping and cheering)* Yay!
Good Little Red 2:	Oh thank you.
Old Wolf:	Hello. I'm the Big Bad Wolf.
All:	*(Boo and hiss in melodrama fashion)* Boo. Hiss.
Old Wolf:	Oh be quiet.
Narrator 3:	But suddenly, the wolf didn't feel so good …
Old Wolf:	Uh oh, heart attack!

Dies of a heart attack.

Doctor:	*(Coming forward and checking Old Wolf's pulse)* Yep. He's dead.

6

| **All:** | (Clapping and cheering) Yay! |

Everyone skips around the stage, singing.

| **All:** | Who's afraid of the big bad wolf,
the big bad wolf, the big bad wolf?
Who's afraid of the big bad wolf?
La La La La La! |

Freeze as forest and woodland creatures.

Scene 4 ——————————

| **TV Star Little Red:** | Hello. I'm … |

The Fans interrupt her.

Fan 1:	(Excited) Hey look! It's Little Red Riding Hood.
Fan 2:	Can I have your autograph?
Fan 3:	Me too? I'm a big fan.

Fans line up as TV Star Little Red signs their autograph books.

Fan 1:	I've got everyone's autograph. I've even got [name a famous person]
Fan 2:	Yeah, well I've got [name another famous person]
Fan 3:	Me too. I've got [famous person]
TV Star Little Red:	Well I must be going to Grandma's house now. Bye.
Fan 1:	Bye.

Fan 2:	Thanks for the autographs.
Fan 3:	Watch out for 'The Wolf'.
TV Star Little Red:	'The Wolf'? Who's afraid of him?
All 3 Fans:	Me!

Everyone skips around the stage, singing.

All:	Who's afraid of the big bad wolf, the big bad wolf, the big bad wolf? Who's afraid of the big bad wolf? La La La La La!

Freeze as forest and woodland creatures.

Scene 5 _____

Piggy 1:	Hello! I'm Piggy Number One And I like having lots of fun. I like to run and skip and draw, I'm going to build my house of straw.
Piggy 2:	Hello! I'm Piggy Number Two I think I know just what to do. I like to eat things quick quick quick, I'm going to build my house of sticks.

Piggy 3:  Hello, I'm Piggy Number Three
I'm very clever you can see.
No straw for me, no twigs or sticks.
I'm going to build my house with
bricks.

Little Piggy Wolf: *(To Piggy 1)* Little pig, little pig. Let
me come in.

Piggy 1: No No. Not by the hair on my
chinny chin chin.

Little Piggy Wolf: Then I'll huff and I'll puff and I'll
blow your house in.

Wolf blows. Piggy 1 squeals and bobs down.

Little Piggy Wolf: *(To Piggy 2)* Little pig, little pig. Let
me come in.

Piggy 2: No No. Not by the hair on my
chinny chin chin.

Little Piggy Wolf: Then I'll huff and I'll puff and I'll
blow your house in.

Wolf blows. Piggy 2 squeals and bobs down.

Little Piggy Wolf:	*(To Piggy 3)* Little pig, little pig. Let me come in.
Piggy 3:	No No. Not by the hair on my chinny chin chin.
Little Piggy Wolf:	Then I'll huff and I'll puff and I'll blow your house in.
Special 1:	*(Steps forward and taps Wolf on the shoulder)* Excuse me.
Little Piggy Wolf:	*(Getting angry)* What is it? Can't you see I'm busy?
Special 1:	You're in the wrong play.
Little Piggy Wolf:	What?!
Special 1:	This is the story of Little Red Riding Hood, *not* The Three Little Pigs.
Little Piggy Wolf:	Oh!
Piggy 1, 2 and 3:	*(Together)* Yippee!!!

Everyone skips around the stage again, singing.

All:	Who's afraid of the big bad wolf, the big bad wolf, the big bad wolf? Who's afraid of the big bad wolf? La La La La La!

Freeze as forest and woodland creatures.

Narrator 4:	This is the story of Little Red Riding Hood.
Bad Little Red 2:	Hello. I'm Little Red Riding Hood and this is my Grandma.
Mad Granny 2:	Yes, what is it? What do you want?
Bad Little Red 2:	Grandma, what great big *eyes* you have.
Mad Granny 2:	That's because I'm wearing glasses.
Bad Little Red 2:	Grandma, what great big *ears* you have.
Mad Granny 2:	That's because I'm wearing earrings.
Bad Little Red 2:	Grandma, what great big *teeth* you have.
Mad Granny 2:	That's because I've got false teeth, you idiot. Now go away and stop picking on me.

Everyone skips around the stage again, singing.

All:	Who's afraid of the big bad wolf, the big bad wolf, the big bad wolf? Who's afraid of the big bad wolf? La La La La La!

Freeze as forest and woodland creatures.

Scene 7

Narrator 5:	This is the story of Little Red Riding Hood.
Dancing Little Red:	Hello. I'm Little Red Riding Hood.
All:	*(Clapping and cheering)* Yay!
Dancing Little Red:	Oh thank you.
Dancing Wolf:	Hello. I'm the Big Bad Wolf.
All:	*(Boo and hiss in melodrama fashion)* Boo. Hiss.
Dancing Wolf:	Oh be quiet.
Old Granny 1:	I'm blind, I'm old, I'm deaf, I'm dumb. My teeth are gone, can't eat a crumb. I'm grandma … Get the picture?
Dancing Wolf:	I'm hungry … Get the picture?
Old Granny 1:	Aaahhh!!! *(Grandma bobs down.)*

Narrator 5:	But who's this walking in the wood? Oh no, it's Little Red Riding Hood. Come to see her Grandma dear. Does she know the Wolf is here?
Dancing Little Red:	Grandma, what great big *eyes* you have.
Dancing Wolf:	All the better to see you with, my dear.
Dancing Little Red:	But Grandma, what great big *ears* you have.
Dancing Wolf:	All the better to hear you with, my dear.
Dancing Little Red:	But Grandma, what a great big *nose* you have.
Dancing Wolf:	All the better to smell you with, my dear.
Dancing Little Red:	But Grandma, what a lovely pair of *shoes* you're wearing.
Dancing Wolf:	Do you really think so?
Dancing Little Red:	Yes.
Dancing Wolf:	Well I like your red cape.
Dancing Little Red:	Thank you. I'm going to a *(Name favourite group)* concert. Would you like to come?

Dancing Wolf:	Yes please.
Dancing Little Red:	I love [*favourite group*].
Dancing Wolf:	Me too!

Dancing Wolf and Dancing Little Red do a short routine together of their favourite group.

Dancing Wolf:	That was fun.
Dancing Little Red:	Shall we do it again?
All:	No!

Everyone skips around the stage again, singing.

All:	Who's afraid of the big bad wolf, the big bad wolf, the big bad wolf? Who's afraid of the big bad wolf? La La La La La!

Freeze as forest and woodland creatures.

Scene 8

Narrator 6:	This is the story of Little Red Riding Hood.
Good Little Red 3:	Hello. I'm Little Red Riding Hood.
All:	*(Clapping and cheering)* Yay!
Good Little Red 3:	Oh thank you.
Bad Wolf 2:	Hello. I'm the Big Bad Wolf.
All:	*(Boo and hiss in melodrama fashion)* Boo. Hiss.
Bad Wolf 2:	Oh be quiet.

14

Old Granny 2:	I'm blind, I'm old, I'm deaf, I'm dumb. My teeth are gone, can't eat a crumb. I'm grandma … Get the picture?
Bad Wolf 2:	I'm hungry … Get the picture?
Old Granny 2:	Aaahhh!!! *(Grandma bobs down.)*
Narrator 6:	But who's this walking in the wood? Oh no, it's Little Red Riding Hood. Come to see her Grandma dear. She doesn't know the Wolf is here …
Good Little Red 3:	Grandma, what great big *eyes* you have.
Bad Wolf 2:	All the better to see you with, my dear.
Good Little Red 3:	But Grandma, what great big *ears* you have.
Bad Wolf 2:	All the better to hear you with, my dear.
Good Little Red 3:	But Grandma, what a great big *nose* you have.
Bad Wolf 2:	Will you hurry up and get to teeth! After nose is teeth. Grandma, what great big teeth you have. I can't work with this. *(Stomps foot)* Where's my agent?
Good Little Red 3:	Alright, alright. Grandma, what great big TEETH you have.

15

Bad Wolf 2:	Thank you. All the better to eat you with.
Good Little Red 3:	Aaahhh!!!

Bad Wolf 2 growls at Good Little Red 3 and goes to eat her, but gets stopped by the Woodcutter.

Woodcutter:	Hold it right there, Mister.
Bad Wolf 2:	Who are you?
Woodcutter:	I'm the Woodcutter and it's my job to see that you stop eating people.
Bad Wolf 2:	Uh Oh!
Woodcutter:	Take that.

In slow motion the Woodcutter karate chops Bad Wolf 2, who does a big dying scene.

Doctor:	*(Coming forward and checking Bad Wolf 2's pulse)* Yep. He's dead.
All:	*(Clapping and cheering)* Yay!

Everyone skips around the stage, singing.

All:	Ding Dong the wolf is dead, the wolf is dead, the wolf is dead … Ding Dong the wolf is dead, La La La La La!

Freeze.

Special 2:	But that's from the *The Wizard of Oz*.
All:	We know!
Special 2:	Oh.
	THE END

16